CONTENTS

CONTENTS

Harry

Niall

I ♥ 1D

One Direction are...

Fun

Talented

Immense

Brilliant

Gorgeous

Creative

Unique

Cool

Amazing

Fun

The Niall File

Name: Niall James Horan

Born: 13th September 1993

Star Sign: Virgo

Hair: Blonde

Eyes: Blue

Shoe Size: 8

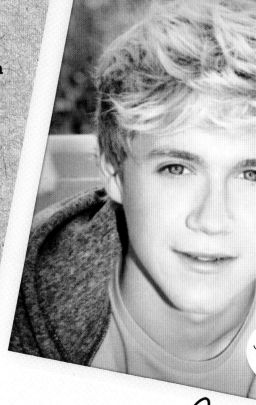

I ♥ NIALL

Just call me 'Nialler'!

NIALL ♥ S ...

- ♥ Oriental Food
- ♥ Football
- ♥ Playing the guitar

And another thing... He's a big fan of Michael Bublé and counts the Canadian crooner's hit 'Crazy Love' as one of his fave tracks.

NIALL
IN A NUTSHELL:

- Dedicated
- Energetic
- Fun-loving

The Harry File

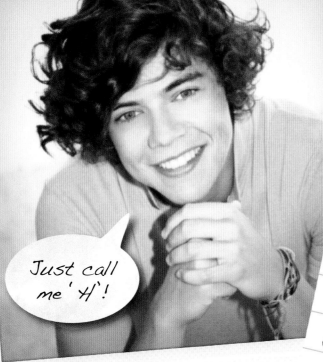

Just call me 'H'!

I ♥ HARRY

HARRY ♥S ...

♥ Back massages

♥ His mum, Anne

♥ Tacos

Name: Harry Edward Styles

Born: 1st February 1994

Star Sign: Aquarius

Hair: Brown

Eyes: Green

Shoe Size: 10.5

And another thing...
Harry's hair wasn't always curly. He had straight hair for the first years of his life.

HARRY
IN A NUTSHELL:

- Charming
- Cheeky
- Confident

The Liam File

Name: Liam James Payne

Born: 29th August 1993

Star Sign: Virgo

Hair: Brown

Eyes: Brown

Shoe Size: 8

Just call me 'Daddy Direction'!

LIAM ♥ S ...

- *Going Bowling*
- *Shopping in 'All Saints'*
- *Turtles - he has two called Boris and Archimedes*

And another thing... Liam was born prematurely, with complications and until recently had just one functioning kidney. An ultrasound scan in August 2012 revealed however that both kidneys are now functioning. Yay!

LIAM
IN A NUTSHELL:

- *Supportive*
- *Focused*
- *Athletic*

Just call me ' Luigi'!

I ♥ LOUIS

LOUIS ♥ S ...

♥ Computer Games

♥ Pizza

♥ Long-term buddy, Stan

And another thing... Hard-worker Louis had a series of part-time jobs as a youngster, including serving popcorn at his local cinema and stacking shelves at Toys 'R' Us.

Name:	Louis William Tomlinson
Born:	24th December 1991
Star Sign:	Capricorn
Hair:	Brown
Eyes:	Blue
Shoe Size:	9.5

LOUIS
IN A NUTSHELL:

- Mischievous
- Stylish
- Loyal

The Zayn File

Name: Zayn Javadd Malik

Born: 12th January 1993

Star Sign: Capricorn

Hair: Black

Eyes: Brown

Shoe Size: 8.5

Just call me 'Zay'!

I ♥ NIALL

ZAYN ♥ S ...

- Drawing
- Watching 'Family Guy'
- Long lie-ins

And another thing... Zayn is a voracious reader who, age 8 had a reading age of 18. He got an A in his English GCSE, which he sat a year early.

ZAYN
IN A NUTSHELL:

- Creative
- Quiet
- Sensitive

My File

^ *YOUR PICTURE HERE*

Just call me ....

^ *YOUR SIGNATURE HERE*

I ♥

♥
♥
♥

And another thing...

Name: ....

Born: ....

Star Sign: ....

Hair: ....

Eyes: ....

Shoe Size: ....

ME
IN A NUTSHELL:

● ....
● ....
● ....

I ♥ ONE DIRECTION

Put your super-fan status to the test and see how much you really know about One Direction. Tick 'TRUE' or 'FALSE' next to each statement.

1. One Direction met the Queen after the Royal Variety Performance in 2012.

TRUE ☐
FALSE ☐

2. Harry went to private school.

TRUE ☐
FALSE ☐

3. Harry was once in a band called White Eagle.

TRUE ☐
FALSE ☐

4. Louis used to work in a football stadium.

TRUE ☐
FALSE ☐

5. Liam has a younger brother called Gary.

TRUE ☐
FALSE ☐

6. Two of the band members have the same middle name.

TRUE ☐
FALSE ☐

7. One Direction made USA music history when both their first two albums debuted at the top of the American chart.

TRUE ☐
FALSE ☐

8. Zayn used to work as a receptionist at a modelling agency.

TRUE ☐
FALSE ☐

9. Harry is the oldest member of One Direction.

TRUE ☐
FALSE ☐

10. The One Direction boys were brought together on a famous BBC show.

TRUE ☐
FALSE ☐

Tell the ONE DIRECTION Story

One Direction got together in 2010, when five unknown lads took a chance and entered the biggest music competition in the country. **How much do you know about what happened next? Use the words at the bottom of the page to complete the band's amazing story.**

Harry, Liam, Niall, Zayn and Louis auditioned for _____ separately, but _____ asked them to form a group. They were surprised, but they all knew that they had to take the opportunity. Before long they were best friends.

The boys had a fantastic time on the show, and although they came third, they were already getting bags of fan mail! It was clear that **One Direction** had an exciting future ahead. When they were signed to _____'s record company, they knew that their dreams had come true.

One Direction went on tour across the UK and _____, and everywhere they went they gained more fans. They released their first album _____ in autumn 2011, and their first single '_____' became the biggest pre-order in Sony's single history. It went in at number one in the UK and Irish charts as soon as it was on iTunes.

Next, the guys set out to conquer _____. Fans lined the streets wherever they went, and in March 2012, Up All Night entered the US Billboard 200 chart at number ___. The boys had cracked the States.

All across the world, people went **One Direction** mad! Up All Night went to number one in 17 countries. With more tours planned and another album in the pipeline, **One Direction** has truly become a global phenomenon!

America • Ireland • one • the Judges • Simon Cowell
The X Factor • Up All Night • What Makes You Beautiful

Moving in the

One Direction's journey from obscurity to their current position as the world's biggest boy-band has been nothing short of miraculous. Here's how it happened.

In 2010, five young men *from the four corners of the UK and Ireland, nervously auditioned for places on the reality show The X Factor. At that point they had nothing in common but a shared passion for music and the mutual dream of fame and fortune. Luckily for us all however, guest judge and former Pussy Cat Doll, Nicole Scherzinger, spotted their combined potential and suggested putting all five soloists together as a band, to compete in Simon Cowell's ' groups' category.*

Despite having just five weeks *in which to get to know each other and learn to harmonise, the boys flew through to the live shows, after wowing formidable judge and music industry guru Cowell. One Direction placed 3rd in the competition but ultimately triumphed by clinching a coveted record deal with Simon Cowell's 'Syco Records' label in January 2011.*

Right Direction

Eight months later the first single *from their album 'Up All Night' was released. 'What Makes You Beautiful' was an instant smash, entering the charts at number 1. It has gone on to become one of the highest selling singles of all time.*

It is, however, the group's success Stateside, *which really sets One Direction apart from other boy-bands and indeed most other UK artists. In November 2011 Columbia Records in North America snapped them up and since then their career in the US has skyrocketed.*

From humble beginnings *as five, cute, boys-next-door, Harry, Niall, Louis, Zayn and Liam have gone on to achieve international success and acclaim on an unimaginable scale. With two studio albums, two best-selling books and a sell-out world tour under their belt, these boys are definitely moving in the right direction.*

So what makes YOU tick? Are you loopy about Liam or nuts about Niall? Check out our alphabetical guide to being a Directioner!

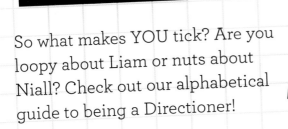

A is for … **Attitude!** - A Directioner always thinks positive.

B is for … **Believing** - Always believe that you can achieve your aims.

C is for … **Carrots** – every Directioner knows why!

D is for … **Dreams** – a Directioner's dreams are all about the band.

E is for … **Excited** - No, make that SUPER-EXCITED to be reading about your fave band!

F is for … **Favourite** – every Directioner has a secret favourite member of the band.

G is for … **Guitar** – we love the instrument Niall plays.

H is for … **Harry's hair!** - It's so famous that it's got its own fanbase!

I is for … **Ireland** – Niall's homeland and a dream destination for Directioners.

J is for … **Jimmy** - as in 'No, Jimmy protested'. And if you know who said that, you've been a Directioner from day one!

...a Directioner

K is for ... **Keep trying** – One Direction didn't give up, even when it seemed as if their X Factor dream was over.

L is for ... **Liam and Louis** – we can't choose between them!

M is for ... **Music** – what would we do without it?

N is for ... **Niall** – is he your fave?

O is for ... **Obsessed** - Who, us?

P is for ... **Passion** – we totally admire the guys' passion for music.

Q is for ... **Questions** – we all have a long list of things.

R is for ... **Real** – the lads want their fans to keep it real and be true to themselves.

S is for ... **Simon Cowell** – let's face it, without him the Directioners' world wouldn't exist. We're grateful to him for life!

T is for ... **Tour** – we can't wait for the next one!

U is for ... **Universally loved** - Yep, the lads have fans across the globe and, let's face it, probably on other planets too. **One Direction** Infection!

V is for ... **Voices** – the lads sing even better than they look!

W is for ... **'What Makes You Beautiful'** – the song that made you fall in love with One Direction.

X is for ... **Kisses** - A true Directioner sends plenty of them to the boys!

Y is for ... **'Yeah buddie'** – one of Niall's fave tweets and a great way for a Directioner to say 'YES'!

Z is for ... **Zayn** - the quiet, mysterious one of the band.

My 1D Story

It probably feels as if One Direction has always been part of your life but can you remember the first time you ever saw or heard about them? Here's your chance to reminisce about discovering the band and your personal journey to true Directioner fan status.

The first time I ever saw or heard about 1D ....

....

The thing I loved about them most was

....

My fave group member is...

....

I like him best because...

....

I always remember when...

....

I voted for them on The X Factor .... times!

I became a true Directioner when...

....

My most memorable 1D performance was...

....

My most treasured 1D-related possessions are...

....

Use this space to create a **1D** memory page – stick in your fave cuttings about the group, pictures from magazines, snaps of you and friends wearing **One Direction** memorabilia.

I ♥ HARRY
ZAYN
NIALL
LOUIS
LIAM

I ♥ 1D

ACCESS ALL AREAS!
VIP PASS 1D
ONE DIRECTION

HEROES

Each of the **One Direction** boys has a hero in the music industry – people who inspire them to be the best they can be. Who is your hero? Write down their name and explain why they inspire you.

My Hero is ....

They inspire inspire me because ....

ELVIS PRESLEY

Michael Jackson

GARY BARLOW

MICHAEL BUBLÉ

ROBBIE WILLIAMS

Make Your Own ALBUM

These are some of **One Direction's** most memorable singles. Do you know them all? List your favourite 12 and create your personal greatest hits album!

Back for You
C'mon, C'mon
Change My Mind
Everything About You
Gotta Be You
Heart Attack
I Want
I Wish
I Would
Kiss You
Last First Kiss
Little Things
Live While We're Young
More than This
One Thing
Over Again
Rock Me
Same Mistakes
Save You Tonight
Stole My Heart
Summer Love
Taken
Tell Me a Lie
They Don't Know About Us
Up All Night
What Makes You Beautiful

My Greatest Hits Album

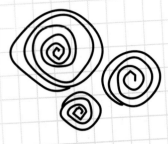

BFFs

The boys have been best buds since spending their first weeks as a group together at Harry's step-dad's house, where they bonded over their love of music and practical jokes.

For three years they've done everything together, from shopping and surfing, to sea fishing and rollercoaster riding. Here's what they have to say about their enduring and touching friendships.

> "My boys have become the best four friends/brothers I have. You've made this the most amazing and exciting time ever and it would be pointless without you."
> *Liam*

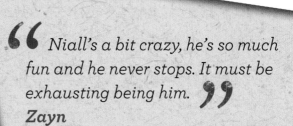

> "Niall's a bit crazy, he's so much fun and he never stops. It must be exhausting being him."
> *Zayn*

> "At boot camp Liam was quite different. Quiet, sensible, kept to himself. But after a while he blossomed into this fine young man."
> *Niall*

"Wouldn't mind a good heart to heart with @zaynmalik right now! Missing you man!"
Louis, via Twitter

"It's incredible that we all choose to spend extra time with each other after the all-day sessions!"
Harry

"At boot camp I had a photo taken with Harry because I knew he was going to be famous. I even gave him a hug and told him not to worry because I knew he'd be fine."
Louis

"I bonded with Louis really quickly because he's like me in a lot of ways, but I also had the most arguments with him for the same reason."
Zayn

"Liam was probably the person I got on best with because he's quite serious and focused."
Zayn

"It all worked out naturally – we all just got on and instantly became friends."
Niall

"New York! What a place! Havin' great craic with the lads. @zaynmalik just walked into a filing cabinet. Ha! Ha! Ha!"
Niall, via Twitter

"Looking forward to watching @Louis_Tomlinson support Blue Bell Wood, it's a great cause. He's worked hard and you can still get tickets."
Harry, via Twitter

NAME *that*

How well do you know **One Direction's** videos? Read these crazy clues and name each song. Can you also identify the year that each video was released?

 A. Should Zayn be running along those railway tracks?

Song: _____

Year: _____

 B. Who turned the studio black and white?

Song: _____

Year: _____

SONG

C. Harry hit the tiger!

Song: _____

Year: _____

D. Loving the sofa on stage!

Song: _____

Year: _____

E. London baby!

Song: _____

Year: _____

F. Every Directioner wants to be in that camper van!

Song: _____

Year: _____

MY BFFs

Whoever your BFFs are, we bet you bond over your love and admiration for the boys. Use these pages to remind you just why you love your friends.

My friend ....

We have been friends for ....

We met ....

She/he is totally awesome because

....

My favourite friendship memory is

....

My friend's fave 1D member is ....

....

If she/he had a day with 1D she/
he would ....

....

Her/his most precious 1D item is

....

My mate ....

We have been friends for ....

We met ....

She/he is absolutely amazing

because ....

My favourite friendship memory is

....

My friend's fave 1D member is ....

....

If she/he had a day with 1D she/he

would ....

....

Her/his most precious 1D item is

....

My pal ....

We have been friends for ....

We met ....

She/he is so cool because ....

....

My favourite friendship memory is

....

My friend's fave 1D member is ......

....

If she/he had a day with 1D she/
he would ....

....

Her/his most precious 1D item is

....

My buddy ....

We have been friends for ....

We met ....

She/he is fabulous fun because

....

My favourite friendship memory is

....

My friend's fave 1D member is ......

....

If she/he had a day with 1D she/
he would ....

....

Her/his most precious 1D item is

....

ACCESS ALL AREAS!

VIP PASS 1D

ONE DIRECTION

I ♥ 1D

ONE DIRECTIO
One Direction Preser
ONE DIRECTION
PLUS SPECIAL GUESTS
(VIP) FRONT ROW

Enter Via Door:2
56780753547

ONE DIRECTION
56780753547

ONE DIRECTION
STICKER JIGSAW

DISASTER! This gorgeous snap of the guys is incomplete.
Use your stickers to complete this jaw-dropping jigsaw.

SPOT THE DIFFERENCE

Check out these heart-melting pictures of Harry. Do you think they're exactly the same? Look again! There are ten differences between them. Grab a red pen and draw a circle around each difference you find.

1D

1D Starstruck

Since finding fame, the boys from One Direction have rubbed shoulders with all sorts of famous people. Some have become close friends of the group, but some A-listers, still have the power to leave the boys starstruck.

Niall kissed a girl and he liked it! Getting up close and personal with friend Katy Perry at the MTV VMAs in LA. Guest judge Katy, put Niall through his early audition round and is a friend and supporter of the group.

Louis knew funny-guy James from his early acting days and went to his wedding. James is now part of the 1D family – even dispensing advice on relationships.

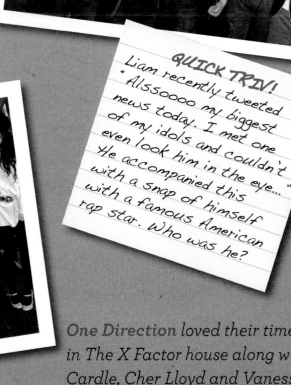

One Direction loved their time living in The X Factor house along with Matt Cardle, Cher Lloyd and Vanessa Ferguson.

Boy-bands of the world unite. Shane and Nicky from Westlife are glad to share their knowledge and experience.

The X Factor Host Dermot O'Leary remains a close friend and the busy boys often bump into him at events like the GQ Awards

QUICK TRIV!
Niall admitted one very famous American lady who is definitely 'First' on his list of amazing women. Who is she?

Harry and rising star Conor Maynard, swap notes on fame.

^ YOUR PICTURE HERE

Have you ever been starstruck? Name the celeb you met or stick your photo in here!

....

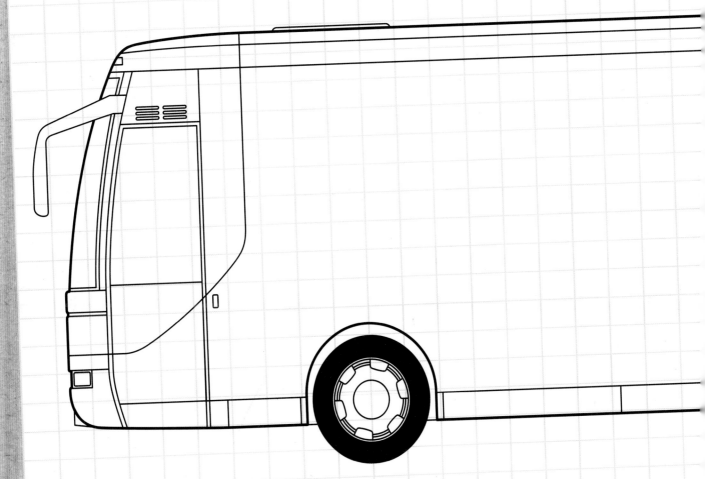

Space for instruments

Space for stage equipment

ROCK

Super-comfy sofas!

BUS FOR THE BOYS

If you were designing a tour bus for One Direction, what great features would you include? Remember, they'll spend loads of time here while they're on tour, so give them a few home comforts for their journeys! We've added a few questions and ideas to get you started . . .

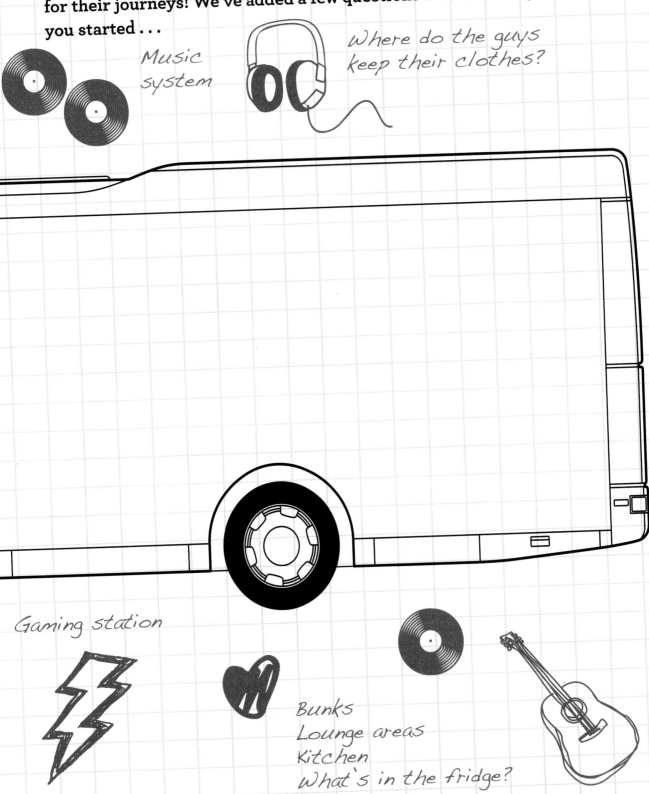

Music system

Where do the guys keep their clothes?

Gaming station

Bunks
Lounge areas
Kitchen
What's in the fridge?

IN JULY AND AUGUST 2012, *One Direction*, like the rest of us, found themselves swept up in Olympic Fever.

As the Games began, they discussed their mounting excitement with Zayn tweeting, 'Don't know if it's just me, but the excitement in London is unbelievable! It's gonna be a great games.' Liam commented 'If I wasn't in One Drection, running the Olympics would have been my dream :)'.

Days before the closing ceremony, the rumour mill – which had long been churning with gossip about a possible 1D appearance - went into overdrive, when the boys flew into town for secret rehearsals and tweeted a snap of themselves with the Olympic torch, backstage.

Having spent much of the year in the States it was great for the boys to return home and to take up a once-in-a-lifetime opportunity to perform at London 2012.

When they weren't rehearsing, the boys made sure they supported the British athletes. Louis and girlfriend Eleanor Calder popped up poolside to lend support to diver Tom Daley in his event. They even took cute snaps of themselves draped in the union flag. Awww!

When the incredible Games came to a close, the rumours were finally proven true, when the boys swept into the stadium aboard a flat-bed truck, singing their mega-hit 'What Makes You Beautiful'. The noise in the filled-to-capacity arena was electric. 300 million viewers worldwide watched the boys sing their hearts out in the biggest ever performance.
It was a perfect moment.

I ♥ 1D

SUMMER

The Greatest Show on Earth

Did you go to the Olympics?
If so which events did you catch?
Create a nostalgia page here
with your tickets, photos and
memories of **London 2012.**

I ♥ ONE DIRECTION

Fashion Focus

If you're lucky enough to get tickets to a One Direction gig, you need to dress to impress! Grab some colouring pens and design your dream outfit.

ODD ONE OUT

There's only one Liam! But that doesn't stop others from trying to copy him. **Look closely at these pictures. Can you pick out the real Liam?**

1

2

3

4

5

6

7

1D

39

1D STAR SUDOKU

The 1D lads love intelligent girls. Test your smarts with this fun puzzle. Every row, column and mini grid of six squares, must contain each of the band members plus the 1D logo. Write their names or sketch them in the correct places.

Missing Lyrics

Been playing the boys' latest album on repeat since you got it? Sure, you have. But how well do you really know each song? Fill in the blanks on the song sheet to complete the lyrics. If you need a clue, the words are jumbled up along the bottom of the page.

LITTLE THINGS

Your .... fits in mine,
Like it's .... just for me,
But .... this in mind,
It was meant to ....

And I'm joining up the .... with the
.... on your cheeks
And it all makes .... to me.

I know you've never ....,
The .... by your eyes when you ....,
You've never loved,
Your stomach or your ....,
The .... in your back at the bottom of
.... spine,
But I'll love them ....

I won't let these little things .... out of
my ....
But if I do, it's ....
...................., it's you they .... up to
I'm in love with you and all these little things.

You can't go to bed without a ....
....,
Maybe that's the reason that you .... in
your sleep,
And all those .... conversations are the
.... that I keep,
Though it makes .... sense to me.

I know you've never loved the sound of your
.... on tape,
You never ....,
To know how much you ....,
You still have to .... into your jeans,
But you're perfect to me.

I won't let these little things slip out of my
mouth,
But if it's true, it's you,
Oh, it's you, they add up to.
I'm in love with you and all these little things.

You'll never love yourself .... as much as
I love you,
You'll never .... yourself right ....,
but I want you to.
If I let you know, I'm .... for you,
Maybe you'll love yourself .... I love you,
oh...

REPEAT CHORUS

ONE DIRECTION

ONE FUTURE!

Do you read your horoscope every day, or do you think that you control your own destiny? Whatever the future holds, check out these fun peeks into your character and the highs and lows of the next twelve months.

ARIES

Perfect partner: Leo
Dating disaster: Pisces
Firm friends: Sagittarius

Five words that describe you:
Passionate, adventurous, competitive, honest, direct

Your future: Some exciting new adventures are heading your way in springtime!

TAURUS

Perfect partner: Virgo
Dating disaster: Aquarius
Firm friends: Capricorn

Five words that describe you:
Reliable, stable, stubborn, physical, affectionate

Your future: You'll have a difficult patch in mid-summer, but it'll all be sorted by autumn.

GEMINI

Perfect partner: Libra
Dating disaster: Cancer
Firm friends: Aquarius

Five words that describe you:
Witty, unpredictable, curious, impatient, changeable

Your future: Christmas time will be festive and fantastic for you this year.

CANCER

Perfect partner: Scorpio
Dating disaster: Gemini
Firm friends: Pisces

Five words that describe you: Emotional, caring, practical, nostalgic, indirect

Your future: In the second half of the year, you'll be feeling super-positive and confident!

LEO

Perfect partner: Aries
Dating disaster: Gemini
Firm friends: Sagittarius

Five words that describe you: Leader, proud, powerful, sociable, motivated

Your future: You'll have a great time doing some travelling in late spring.

VIRGO

Perfect partner: Pisces
Dating disaster: Libra
Firm friends: Capricorn

Five words that describe you: Sensitive, calming, perfectionist, critical, shy

Your future: June will turn you into a social butterfly!

LIBRA

Perfect partner: Gemini
Dating disaster: Virgo
Firm friends: Aquarius
Five words that describe you: Passionate, comforting, friendly, fair, intuitive
Your future: Late summer and early autumn will turn you into a fashion icon!

SAGITTARIUS

Perfect partner: Gemini
Dating disaster: Capricorn
Firm friends: Aries
Five words that describe you: Open, extreme, insecure, impulsive, tough
Your future: Look out for romance from late summer onwards.

AQUARIUS

Perfect partner: Gemini
Dating disaster: Taurus
Firm friends: Libra
Five words that describe you: Cool, interesting, reserved, intellectual, determined
Your future: You'll be facing some extra stress this year, so take time to relax and remember what's important to you.

SCORPIO

Perfect partner: Cancer
Dating disaster: Aries
Firm friends: Virgo
Five words that describe you: Fiery, intense, unforgiving, powerful, intelligent
Your future: The end of the year will mark a new beginning for you.

CAPRICORN

Perfect partner: Cancer
Dating disaster: Sagittarius
Firm friends: Virgo
Five words that describe you: Planner, hard-working, fearful, supportive, steady
Your future: This year holds great potential for you, if you can build your confidence and really start to believe in yourself.

PISCES

Perfect partner: Virgo
Dating disaster: Aries
Firm friends: Cancer
Five words that describe you: Artistic, dreamy, emotional, sensitive, understanding
Your future: There are exciting times ahead! A big surprise is heading your way in the second half of the year.

I ♥ 1D

Take Me Home

It was the most hotly anticipated new album in years. Fans around the globe were on tenterhooks, waiting to see if One Direction could possibly top the success of their debut album, 'Up All Night', which, since its release in September 2011 has sold three million copies and counting.

The group even managed to add to the feverish anticipation by refusing to leak any details to the media. In an interview on US television Liam said, "The success of the first album meant that we were nervous about the second album before we'd heard any of the tunes. But, as soon as the songs started to come in we got really excited and we can't wait for the release." While Zayn added, "We don't want to ruin the surprise for the fans."

Could One Direction possibly come up with songs a catchy as 'WMYB' or 'One Thing'? The lead single, 'Live While We're Young' which was released on 28th September 2012, certainly seemed to indicate that the group had pushed their creativity to another level. It reached number one in almost every country in which it charted and in America it recorded the highest ever one-week opening sales figure for a song by a non-US artist. Would the rest of the album live up to the promise?

On it's release in November 2012, the album landed the No1 spot on the pre-order charts in 50 countries. It sold over a million copies worldwide in the first week in the UK and US and for sure, will continue to be played, played and replayed into ears and hearts around the globe, for years to come.

Take Me Home?

The album title can apparently be read three ways, according to the lads. It reflects how they often feel after months and months on the road. It's also what they want you to do with the album. Finally according to Liam it could mean 'take me home, as in me!' Any offers?

The answer, thankfully, was a resounding 'yes'. The group cleverly harnessed the production skills of top talent including Dr. Luke (Katy Perry's go-to producer). McFly and Ed Sheeran also penned five of the tracks. The result is a foot-tapping rollercoaster featuring everything from anthemic soft-rock ('Summer of Love) to the dancey 'C'mon, C'mon' and the emotional folk creation 'Little Things'.

Which Direction?

Hidden in this grid are fifteen words that Directioners will know and love. Can you find them all?

ALBUMS

COMPETITION

DIRECTIONERS

UP ALL NIGHT

FANS

HARRY

JUDGES

LIAM

LOUIS

LYRICS

NIALL

SINGING

TOUR

TWITTER

ZAYN

A	B	C	D	E	F	T	H	I	J	K	L	M	N	O
D	J	S	G	K	L	O	U	I	S	F	X	N	P	R
J	W	U	T	S	E	U	M	C	A	M	T	S	D	I
I	D	A	D	S	A	R	H	O	R	R	U	P	O	T
L	I	A	M	G	B	I	E	M	S	F	G	B	F	E
S	R	N	W	S	E	M	I	P	O	N	T	T	L	R
F	E	Y	H	I	E	S	M	E	O	H	Q	W	S	A
J	C	E	B	M	G	A	S	T	G	O	F	I	U	V
G	T	K	Z	A	Y	N	H	I	N	F	J	T	K	O
H	I	S	R	B	A	M	N	T	U	H	F	T	L	D
G	O	M	L	F	F	L	N	I	G	F	D	E	Y	V
S	N	G	R	B	L	K	J	O	N	H	A	R	R	Y
D	E	X	Q	A	N	S	I	N	G	I	N	G	I	D
W	R	G	P	J	M	I	Y	T	F	E	F	G	C	J
E	S	U	B	J	Y	T	N	I	A	L	L	J	S	G

SHADOW SPOTTER

If you're a true Directioner, this puzzle will be easy for you! Look at these shadows and identify each one. How fast can you complete the challenge?

PRANK YOU

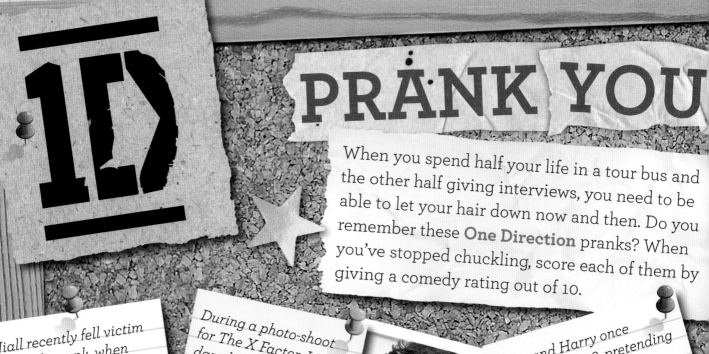

When you spend half your life in a tour bus and the other half giving interviews, you need to be able to let your hair down now and then. Do you remember these **One Direction** pranks? When you've stopped chuckling, score each of them by giving a comedy rating out of 10.

Niall recently fell victim to a mob prank, when the other band members agreed to perform the rap from the TV show Fresh Prince of Bel Air, live on stage, without telling him anything about it.

/10

During a photo-shoot for The X Factor, Liam dared Louis to put his hand on Simon Cowell's very famous bottom. Say cheese, Simon!

Louis and Harry once prank-called 118, pretending to need the number for someone whose surname was Terrrrrrence. Louis: "It's T, it's e, it's r, it's r, 'it's r, 'it's r..." Operator: "How many r's are there? Louis: "six!"

/10

Zayn, Harry, Niall and Louis once taped Liam's mouth shut during an interview due to his inability to stop talking.

/10

In perhaps the most high-profile prank to date, Zayn and Louis tricked the othermembers of the band into thinking that they were going to have to deliver the baby of a TV producer, during an interview for TV station, Nickelodeon.

/10

Harry stunned his stylist Caroline when, in an on-air prank call, during Nick Grimshaw's Radio 1 show, he told her that he liked to wear his sister's crotchless tights on stage and demanded she get him some pairs to take to the U.S. for the tour.

/10

Niall posted pictures on his Twitter page showing himself with purple hair, pretending to have dyed it. In fact, he was just mid-way through a conditioning treatment.

/10

In a marathon live Twitcam prank-athon, Louis attempted to prank call Zayn pretending to be a crazed fan and then, when Zayn rumbled him, he admitted he'd also pranked Rebecca Ferguson and Tom from McFly with bogus fan calls.

/10

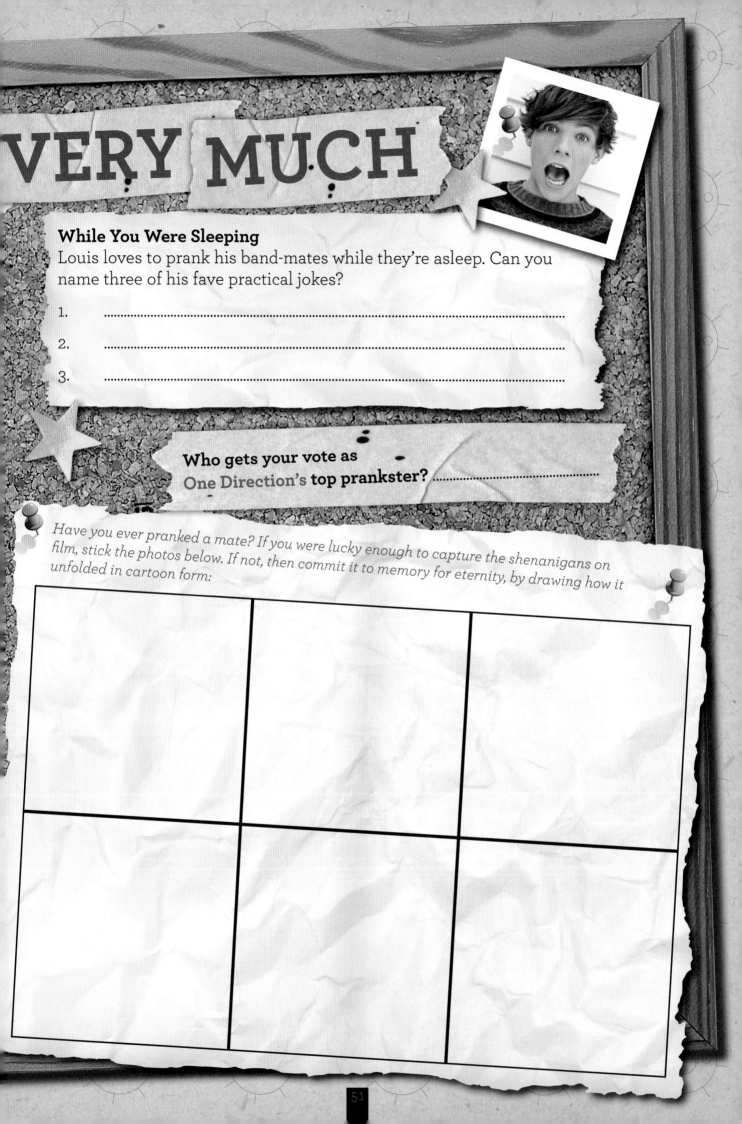

VERY MUCH

While You Were Sleeping

Louis loves to prank his band-mates while they're asleep. Can you name three of his fave practical jokes?

1. ....

2. ....

3. ....

Who gets your vote as One Direction's top prankster? ....

Have you ever pranked a mate? If you were lucky enough to capture the shenanigans on film, stick the photos below. If not, then commit it to memory for eternity, by drawing how it unfolded in cartoon form:

LOVE,

They're five of the most gorgeous and eligible young men on the planet right now. No wonder then, that rumours are constantly circulating about their love lives. Unscramble the girls' names below and match them with the One Directioner they've been (rightly or wrongly) linked to.

1. **DECLARE LOANER**

....
(girls name)

....
(band member name)

2. **REWARDED SPIRE**

....
(girls name)

....
(band member name

3. **NAG EMERY**

....
(girls name)

....
(band member name]

4. **BUCCANEER FORGES**

....
(girls name)

....
(band member name

5. **WEASEL LION**

....
(girls name)

....
(band member name

6. **FLORAS WITTY**

....
(girls name)

....
(band member name

7. **ALLIANCE FROCK**

....
(girls name)

....
(band member name

8. **LEANIDLE RAPZEE**

....
(girls name)

....
(band member name

9. **LOAD MOTIVE**

....
(girls name)

....
(band member name

10. **ARCA LEGENDVEIN**

....
(girls name)

....
(band member name

LOVE, LOVE

Wow! Create your own 2D shrine to the guy of your dreams. Whether you worship at the altar of Harry, think Liam is sent from heaven or (gasp) have another 'real life' boyf, this page is for you to fill with all things 'him'. Think cute pix, doodles and things which remind you...

1D

HIT THE ROAD

WITH ONE DIRECTION!

On the Road...

Back in December 2011 **One Direction** began their inaugural tour. The 'Up All Night' tour visited nine countries on three continents during the eight months of shows. Here are just a few of the highlights...

'Liam serenades his home crowd in Wolverhampton'

'Hello Watford!'
The Up All Night Tour opened in Watford on The 18th December, but just two days later the boys were up in Liam's home territory, playing Wolverhampton Civic Hall.

'Harry whips up the audience in Bournemouth'

Storming Set List
The **One Direction** set list contained most of the hits from their debut album of the same name but with some clever covers thrown in including Natalie Imbruglia's 'Torn' and 'Use Somebody' by The Kings of Leon. In some shows accomplished guitarist Niall thrilled fans with his version of Ed Sheerans hit A-Team

ONE DIRECTION

I ♥ LOUIS

I ♥ NIALL

I ♥ 1D

I ♥ ZAYN

I ♥ LIAM

I ♥ HARRY

I ♥ ONE DIRECTION

ONE DIRECTION
One Direction Presents
ONE DIRECTION
PLUS SPECIAL GUESTS
(VIP) FRONT ROW
Enter Via Door:2
56780753547

A78

ONE DIRECTION

ONE DIRECTION

ONE DIRECTION

I ♥ 1D

1D 1D 1D 1D 1D

Harry

Liam

Louis

Niall

Zayn

I ♥ 1D

I ♥ ONE DIRECTION I ♥ ONE DIRECTION I ♥ ONE DIRECTION

QUICK TRIV!
In 2013 One Direction will kick off their first World tour with dates around the UK and Ireland including the massive O2 Arena in London. Don't miss them!

Lotsa Laughs

In Wellington, New Zealand the boys were on fine form, making fans laugh by swapping outfits with Zayn in Liam's checked shirt, Niall in Louis' stripes and Liam in Zayn's varsity jacket.

QUICK TRIV!
Can you unscramble the name of this British artist who supported 1D on the U.S. leg of their tour?
LOLY RUMS

New Fans

After concerts in Canada and Mexico it was off to the U.S.A. where the lads performed around the country in venues packed with their new American fans.

Not a Clue!

The guys seriously need your help! They've forgotten the name of one of their songs. Solve these clues and then put the letters in the shaded squares together to find the name of the song.

ACROSS

4. Harry entered a Battle of the Bands competition with this group.

8. The band's first song as a group.

9. The name of **One Direction's** first tour.

11. The school musical in which Louis played Danny.

DOWN

1. The song **One Direction** performed at the 2012 Royal Variety Performance.

2. **One Direction's** record label.

3. The country where the band recorded their second album.

5. **One Direction's** mentor on The X Factor.

6. Niall's mother's name.

7. The last word of **One Direction's** debut single.

10. **What are One Direction** most famous for releasing...

ONE DIRECTION
Mystery Guy

Which band member is this? Read the clues and figure out who's hiding in the shadows.

My middle name is JAMES.

I have BLUE eyes.

I talk in my SLEEP.

I can play the GUITAR.

I can speak SPANISH.

My Tour

Have you caught One Direction in concert yet? If so, here's your chance to write down all the incredible memories of the night, in the form of a newspaper review of the show. Don't worry if you've yet to hold that elusive ticket in your hand, just use your creative writing skills to imagine seeing them live.

A NIGHT TO REMEMBER

Review by ....

Picture Perfect

Stick your concert souvenirs here – ticket stubs, photos, brochure pages, the playlist, and the hankie you used to stifle your screams of joy...

ACCESS ALL AREAS!

VIP PASS

1D

ONE DIRECTION

I ♥ 1D

I ♥ LOUIS

I ♥ NIALL

I ♥ ZAYN

I ♥ LIAM

I ♥ HARRY

ONE DIRECTION

Grab a couple of friends and see who can get all the guys' autographs and join them onstage first!

YOU WILL NEED: Dice and a marker for each player

HOW TO PLAY

1. Throw the dice – the highest score starts the game.
2. Move along the squares, making sure that you finish a turn on each autograph.

3. Throw the correct number to reach the tour bus.
4. The winner is the first player to reach the tour bus with all the autographs.

12

11

10

7

8

6

Harry blows you a kiss and you drop your bags. **Go back 3 squares.**

9

5

3

You don't spot the tour bus arriving. Miss a turn.

4

2

THE RULES

- You can move forwards or backwards, but you can't switch directions during a turn.
- You can choose to miss a turn.
- Each player has to finish their turn on each autograph square before they can finish the game. So if Liam's autograph is on square 4, you have to throw a 4 to collect it.
- When you have collected all the autographs, you must throw the correct number to reach the tour bus.

START

1

Both Directions Board Game

13

14

17

18

19

 **20**

The guys dedicate a song to you. **Go forward four squares.**

 **15**

16

Louis winks at you! **Have another turn.**

21

 **24**

23

 **22**

Swap autographs with the player on your right.

25

 **26**

 **27**

28

You've lost your tickets! **Go back to the beginning.**

29

 FINISH **30**

Globetrotting

The boys spend so much time touring, they're rarely at home these days. Keep up with their to-ings and fro-ings by tracking their progress around the globe over the next months.

NORTH AMERICA

SOUTH AMERICA

I ♥ ONE DIRECTION

Geezers

ASIA

EUROPE

AFRICA

ASTRALIA

You could stick dotted stickers on the maps or draw dots on and write the dates they visited. You could also plot your own travels over the past years, on school trips or in summer holidays. See! It's only a matter of time before your globetrotting paths cross!

ONE DIRECTION
How Many Words?

How many words can you make using the letters from:

I'M A DIRECTIONER!

_____   _____
_____   _____
_____   _____
_____   _____
_____   _____
_____   _____
_____   _____
_____   _____

Follow the Fans!

The One Direction boys have performed a fantastic gig and are heading for the tour bus. But the paparazzi are chasing them for photos! Can you help lead them to their tour bus without meeting a single photographer?

DOWN TIME

One of the reasons One Direction work so well as a group is because they genuinely like each other and enjoy each other's company. Despite the number of weeks and months each year that they spend working together, they still love nothing better than hanging out as five mates.

Jam Party

The boys often enjoy jam sessions together. Niall and Liam play guitar, Zayn plays piano and Louis plays both. Harry apparently plays the kazoo! Who knew?

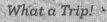

Pedal Power

After the rounds of planes, trains and limos ferrying them around the globe, the One Direction boys love to return to simpler forms of transport including the pushbike. When at Harry's stepdad's they all bike down to the local ice-cream shop and Louis and Liam were recently spotted cruising the streets of London on Boris Bikes.

What a Trip!

Although life must feel like a permanent road trip, the boys wouldn't rule out a One Direction road-trip one day. They have already holidayed together. Louis and Harry enjoy skiing, while all the boys love beach life. While in Sydney Harry, Louis and Liam were pictured sunbathing and swimming off a stunning yacht, in the iconic harbour.

Riding High

The boys love theme parks and while in the U.S. visited Universal Studios Resort in Florida and Six Flags Magic Mountain.

Sport Billies

Like all lads, the One Directioners love to watch sport. While in Auckland, they caught a rugby match between New Zealand and Australia.

How do you spend your weekends?
Create a collage here of your best holidays or days out together. Stick in tickets, brochures or photos.

ONE DIRECTION

Jamming Session

Not only do the One Direction boys sing like a dream, but they're also talented musicians. Follow the lines with your finger to find out who plays what! Then answer the questions below.

ROCK

1. Which two guys could strum a love song on a guitar? _____ _____

2. Who can tinkle the ivories? _____

3. Who plays the triangle? _____

4. Who knows what to do with a kazoo? _____

New Style Directions

In the music industry image is as vital to continued success as talent. Early teens when they came to fame, the lads have had to mature and find their fashion feet in the uncompromising glare of the media spotlight. This section looks at their evolving style.

At the start of their journey - five fresh-faced, raw young lads, arrived at the Very.co.uk Christmas fashion show in 2010. Showing an early interest in fashion while on The X Factor, the lads hadn't yet worked out how to create a strong image to carry them forward.

Then

Now

Fast-forward two years and it's a very different story. The One Direction lads form a slick and stylish unit, blending perfectly in tones of blue, denim and white, yet each bringing his own twist to the band's image. Read on to discover more about each band-member's personal style...

New Directions:

Then

Now

I ♥ HARRY

Hair-y Styles

Hazza's hair has gone from unruly mop, to, well, slightly better tamed mop. The gorgeous wild curls are still there, but they're more artfully arranged these days.

Trackies to Tailoring.

In 2010 Harry's style was all about comfort and he loved slouchy leisurewear. Nowadays the cheeky Northerner is arguably the most dapper member of the group, rarely out of tailoring and if so, carefully casual.

SIGNATURE STYLE

♥ Harry' blazers a trail' in smart tailoring - jackets, blazers and tuxes feature heavily in his fashion portfolio.

♥ Get Shirty - buttoned-up primly, or entirely collarless, Harry rocks a shirt

♥ Accessories - Harry loves to put his own mark on an outfit with quirky accessories, from cute bow-ties, to cravats and pocket handkerchiefs.

New Directions: LOUIS

Then

Now

Hair Hair!

Particularly blessed in the follicle department, Louis has got to grips with his thick locks over the years and is now sporting an über-sophisticated swept-up do. Longer on top and beautifully razored the addition of grooming products gives him that gorgeously mussed up look.

I ♥ LOUIS

SIGNATURE STYLE

💜 Slim fit Chinos – full length or rolled up and in bright hues, these look great on Louis.

💜 Casual tees or crisp white shirts, Louis looks amazing casual or smart!

💜 Beanies – Louis is a big fan of the cosy, woolly hats.

Naval Gazer

Louis has always had a strong sense of style, but has honed his fashion smarts over the years. When something works for Louis he sticks with it. Always a fan of stripes, the stylish guy continues to wear them every which way.

New Directions: LIAM

Then

Now

I ♥ LIAM

Hair today – gone tomorrow.
Liam's early look was the Bieber swoosh, but as he's matured, so have his cuts. The boy from the Midlands has gone through curly, to cropped and is now sporting a shaved 'buzz cut'. With a face like his, why not show it off. We likey!

Boy II Man
Liam has arguably changed the most from the early days of One Direction. His frame has filled out massively and his jawline has become more pronounced. He still prefers the casual look and but he looks sharp in a suit these days.

SIGNATURE STYLE

♥ Contrasting lapels – give a twist to a classic black jacket.

♥ Check him out! – What's not to love about a checked shirt!

♥ Polo shirts – Liam's look works because of its simplicity. He favours classic shapes and pieces such as Ralph Lauren and Lacoste polo shirts.

NIALL

New Directions:

Then

Now

Hair-raising!

Niall's luscious blonde locks are an integral part of his style but when the band was just starting out liked to experiment. At one point he dyed the sides a reddish brown and then flirted with a complete image change. He decided to dye his hair black! Luckily, Simon Cowell managed to talk him out of it. Phew!

I ♥ NIALL

College Boy

Niall has always preferred the informal look. Three years ago he'd throw on a slogan tee with mismatched accessories. Now, he's the epitome of dressed-down chic, looking fresh and stylish in casual separates from brands like Jack Wills and Abercrombie & Fitch.

SIGNATURE STYLE

♥ Hoodies - who said hoodies are for hoodlums? Niall shows how the much maligned leisure item, worn layered up in neutral tones can look smart.

♥ Hi-tops - A staple in Niall's wardrobe, Niall loves bright footwear.

♥ Buttoned Tees - In natural fabrics, these look effortlessly cool.

New Directions:

Then

Now

Well Hair-llo there!

Zayn's hairstyle has been pretty much consistent since the early days until 'Wham!' or should we say 'Zap!' he hit us with his blonde flash, which he slicks into a cool quiff. Style never stands still when you're part of One Direction.

Walk on the Wild Side

Formerly a lover of the chunky cardie, Zayn now treads a careful line between bad boy style and the preppy look, cleverly mixing leather pieces and fitted rock tees with denim and baseball jackets or more formal wear, to give his look an exciting edge.

SIGNATURE STYLE

♥ The Biker Jacket - In black leather or heavy fabrics this trend and Zayn were made for each other.

♥ The Baseball Jacket - Another Malik fave. Zayn wears these in all colour-ways emblazoned with D's for D and M's for Malik.

♥ Statement Accents - From his large stud earrings to his strong-framed glasses, Zayn accents his outfits with stand-out accessories.

GET RHYMING!

The guys are always keen to find fantastic new songwriters. Are you up for the challenge? Grab a pen and write a song that you'd love to hear One Direction sing.

QUIZZICAL QUOTES

Who said that? Match the quote to the band member.
When you know who said what, find the matching
sticker and place it next to the correct quote.

Before you judge
people, judge yourself.

Live life for the moment, because everything
else is uncertain

It's mad to think I didn't know them two years
ago and now they're my best mates.

I'll always defend the
people I love.

We have a choice, to
live or to exist.

ONE DIRECTION

Harry's got a new camera, but he hasn't figured out how to use it yet! Can you identify who's who in each of these backstage snaps?

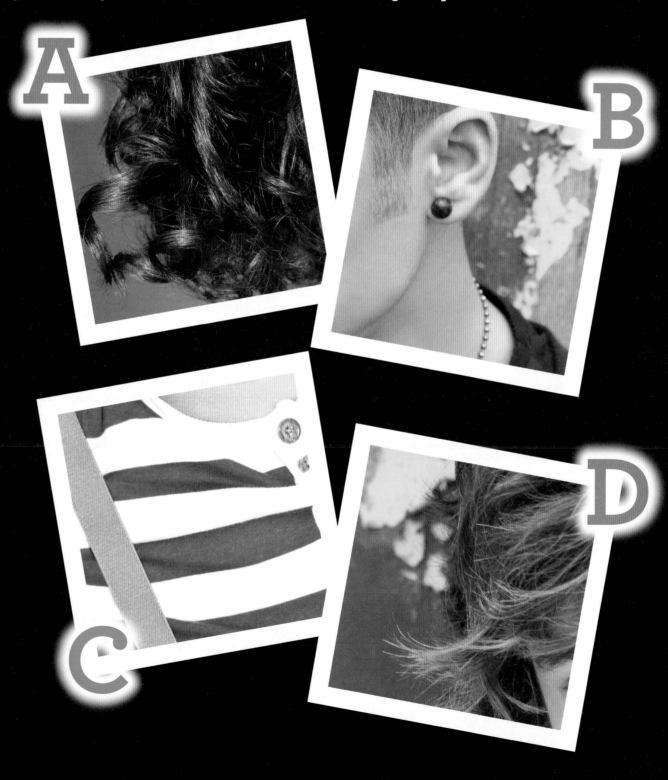

Picture Perfect

Whose Tattoos?

One major One Direction trend which shows no sign of abating is body art. The boys just can't get enough of inking their bodies with quirky quotes and strange symbols. Match up the tattoo fanatic with his particular etchings. Oh, and bear in mind that more than one band-member may sport the same symbol.

'BUT NOTHING I'LL EVER NEED'

MICROPHONE

BIRDCAGE

A PAIR OF SWALLOWS

'WALTER'

THEATRE MASKS

'THINGS I CAN'

'EVERYTHING I EVER WANTED'

CROSSED FINGERS

'THINGS I CAN'T'

'WON'T STOP 'TIL WE SURRENDER'

17 BLACK

A CAPITAL A

PADLOCK

LARGE STAR

'ZAP'

TWO SCREWS

'BE TRUE TO WHO YOU ARE'

A SILVER FERN

A PLAYING CARD

STICK MAN SKATEBOARDING

FOUR CHEVRONS

Which 1D member has been loath to get a tattoo but has hinted and joked about having things inked on his bottom?

A famous British artist tattooed pal Harry with a design. Who was it and what was the design?

Think Ink

What would you like to see gracing Harry's torso, Louis' ankle or Zayn's back?
Sketch your design for the ultimate One Direction inking here. Will it be your
name entwined with hearts and flowers or a majestic whale breaking the surface,
to symbolise the magnitude and beauty of the band? The choice is yours.

ONE DIRECTION

ANAGRAMS

The wacky sentences below are anagrams of producers that have worked with **One Direction.** Do you know enough about the band to figure them all out?

1. CALF LARK

_ _ _ _ _ _ _ _

2. CAVE STEM

_ _ _ _ _ _ _ _

3. AIM YOUR CAB

_ _ _ _ _ _ _ _ _ _

4. STAR QUIT ME

_ _ _ _ _ _ _ _ _ _

5. SHACK BELL

_ _ _ _ _ _ _ _ _

6. JEN BUILT TUNA

_ _ _ _ _ _ _ _ _ _ _

NAME *the* SONG

As a committed DIrectioner, you probably know every word to every 1D song, right? Now it's time to put yourself to the test. This muddled message contains lyrics from ten different One Direction songs. Can you name them all?

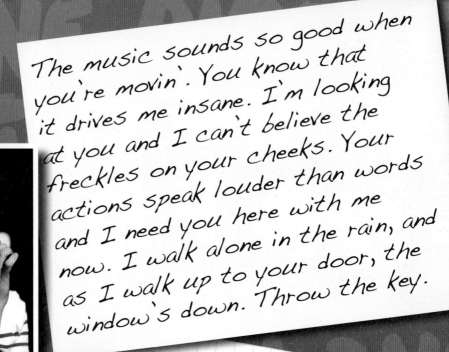

The music sounds so good when you're movin'. You know that it drives me insane. I'm looking at you and I can't believe the freckles on your cheeks. Your actions speak louder than words and I need you here with me now. I walk alone in the rain, and as I walk up to your door, the window's down. Throw the key.

1. _____
2. _____
3. _____
4. _____
5. _____
6. _____
7. _____
8. _____
9. _____
10. _____

My Changing Style

What did you look like back in 2010, when the band came together? You've probably changed a lot since then.

Here's where you plot your personal fashion journey with a cute retrospective of your past looks followed by a peek into your future as a fashionista.

Use this page to stick in shots of yourself, sporting trends which once rocked your world. Then, use the opposite page to take your next style steps. Don't forget to add any photos of you wearing 1D pieces, from to-die-for tees to top-of-the-range trainers.

Create pages from a look-book here to show the styles which are really working for you this season. Create a mood-board using swatches of fabric, cuttings from fashion magazines or sketches of designs you'd love to rock. The One Direction logo should feature heavily, obvs!

I ♥ ZAYN

I ♥ NIALL

I ♥ LIAM

I ♥ 1D

Lookin' good, lady!

ONE DIRECTION

In-Depth

Complete this quiz to find out if you're a super-fan or a super-flop!

 1. What is Harry's full name?

_____

 2. Who once owned a car called Cheryl?

_____

 3. In how many countries did the album Up All Night reach number one?

_____

 4. What is Louis's date of birth?

_____

 5. At which stage of The X Factor was One Direction formed?

_____

 6. Which of the boys was scared of clowns when he was young?

_____

 7. Who thought of the band's name?

_____

 8. For which single did the boys win their first BRIT Award?

_____

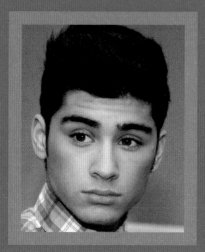

DIRECTIONER

 9. What is Liam's star sign?

_____

 10. Which of the boys sees Justin Timberlake as one of his most important influences?

_____

 11. What is Harry's Twitter username?

_____

 12. In which year was the band formed?

_____

 13. Where did Niall grow up?

_____

If you knew all the answers without looking them up, award yourself an extra ten points.

14. Where was One Direction's first Up All Night tour date?

_____

 15. What is Zayn's full name?

_____

RESULTS

25

You're one serious super-fan! It's because of Directioners like you that the boys are on top of the world.

10-15

Not a bad result, but there's definitely room for improvement. Try the memory test on page 52!

1-10

You love the songs but you don't know enough about the singers. Check out the profile pages and you'll soon be a clued-up Directioner!

Scream if You Love 1D!

One Direction fans are the most loyal – and vocal – set of fans in existence. Check out these devoted Directioners.

Can you see yourself here? If not, don your finest One Direction gear, pick up your 'I heart Niall' placard and get photographed in ultra-fan mode! Now add yourself to the madness.

^ ADD YOUR OWN PIC HERE

COVER STARS

Magazine editors around the world are clamouring to get
One Direction on the cover of their titles. In 2012 the boys made
history by shooting Cosmopolitan magazine's first all-male cover
while Teen Vogue in the US and Fabulous in the UK both ran
incredible collectible covers featuring each of the lads. Snip
headlines from your own back copies of magazines, or
write your own and stick them in, to create an eye-popping mag cover.

CODED MESSAGE

The guys have written a secret message to their most devoted Directioners. Can you crack the riddle, figure out the code and read the note?

RIDDLE

If A is C and C is E, how confusing can this be?

JGA FKTGEVKQPGTU,

YG'F NKMG VQ

VJCPM AQW HQT

CNN AQWT

COCBKPI UWRRQTV

QXGT VJG RCUV

AGCT. AQW OGCP

GXGTAVJKPI VQ WU.

UNCA EQQN!

Now write a reply using the secret code!

Time Traveller

As the boys of One Direction know, a lot can change in a year. Where do you think you'll be in twelve months? What would you like to tell your future self? Use this space to write a letter to yourself. Then check back in a year to read your message!

Place ....

Date ....   Time ....

Dear Me,

....

....

....

....

....

....

....

....

....

....

....

....

....

....

....

....

I can't wait to find out ....

Right now all I can think about is ....

My fave song is ....

My secret crush is ....

My last dream was about ....

My ideal job would be ....

I hope that you are ....

Don't forget ....

I ♥ HARRY
ZAYN
NIALL
LOUIS
LIAM

FAN ART

What's a Directioner's ultimate dream? It's got to be a surprise visit from your favourite band. Complete this poster to advertise a One Direction gig at your house!

ONE

LIVE
IN CONCERT

ONE DIRECTION
One Direction Presents
ONE DIRECTION
PLUS SPECIAL GUESTS
(VIP) FRONT ROW

Enter Via Door:2
56780753547

A78

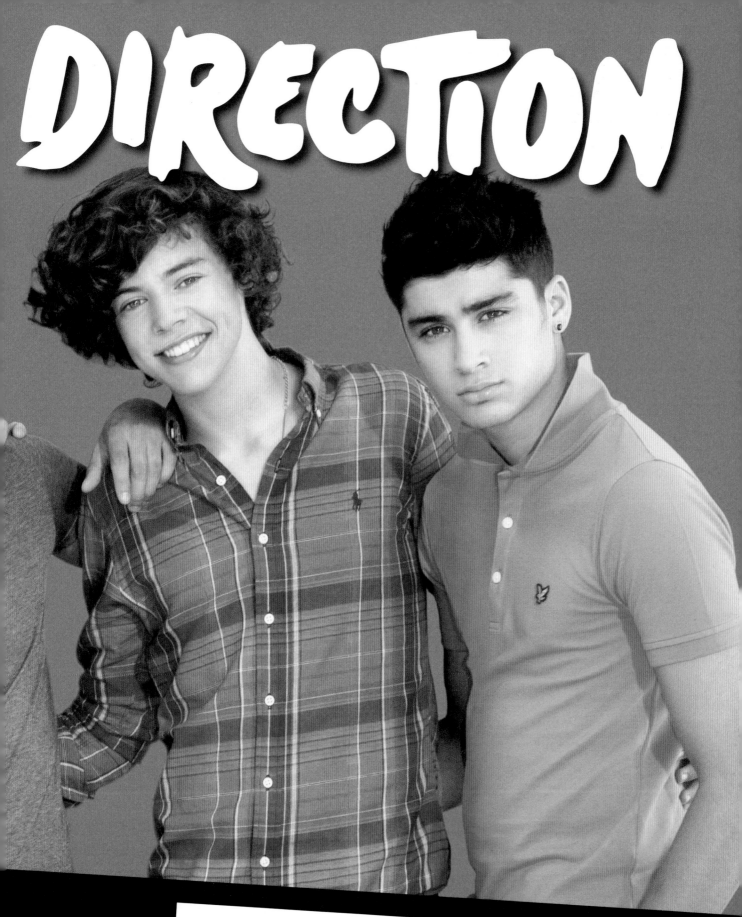

DIRECTION

DATE: ....

TIME: ....

VENUE: ....

BUY YOUR
TICKETS BEFORE
THEY SELL OUT!

And the Winners Are...

The shelves of One Direction's trophy cabinet are literally groaning with the weight of all the plaques, statuettes and trophies they've won. The list is far too long to fit on two measly pages, but here are just few of their proudest moments.

BAMBI AWARDS, NOVEMBER 2012

The lads were delighted to be presented with the award for Pop International Act of the year at the BAMBI awards in Germany.

MTV EUROPE MUSIC AWARDS NOVEMBER 2012

Work commitments meant the lads couldn't be there in person to accept their three awards for Best New Act, Best UK & Ireland Act and Biggest Fans, so they did so via video link. Ahhh, the wonders of technology!

BBC RADIO 1 TEEN AWARDS, OCTOBER 2012

- 'Up All Night' – Best British Album
- 'One Thing' – Best British Single
- Best British Music Act

One Direction were barely off the stage at the BBC Radio 1 Teen Awards, making the trek between seats and stage a whopping three times to collect their trio of gongs. They also topped a fantastic bill which included Taylor Swift, Little Mix and Ne-Yo.

MTV VIDEO MUSIC AWARDS, SEPTEMBER 2012

It was a huge night for One Direction as they took home the gongs for New Artist, Pop Video and Most Share-Worthy Video for 'What Makes You Beautiful'. They also brought the house down with an electrifying performance.

NICKELODEON KIDS' CHOICE AWARDS UK, MARCH 2012

The boys are so popular Stateside that they even managed to swerve a 'gunking' at these awards where nominees and winners are routinely covered in slime while on stage. As well as performing, the boys took home awards for Favourite UK Band and Favourite UK Newcomer. Hurrah!

BRIT AWARDS FEBRUARY 2012

It was their first ever award and what an award it was! A coveted Brit for Best British Single, for 'What Makes You Beautiful' gave them a taste of what was to come including red carpet arrivals, acceptance speeches and after-show parties.

I ♥ ONE DIRECTION

MEMORY TEST

Look carefully at this picture for 60 seconds. Then turn
the page and answer the questions to find out how good your memory really is!

I ♥ ONE DIRECTION

MEMORY TEST

1. Who has tucked his sunglasses into his shirt?

2. Who is Niall sharing a tandem with?

3. Which foot does Louis have on the ground?

4. Which two boys have a basket on the back of their tandem?

5. Who is wearing the darkest trousers?

6. How many boys have bare arms?

7. What colour are Liam's trousers?

8. Which way is Harry leaning?

9. What are the three colours on Zayn's jumper?

10. What lines the background?

Harry

I ♥ HARRY

PAGE 26 - Name that Song:
A. Gotta Be You. B. Little Things
C. Live While We're Young.
D. More Than This. E. One Thing.
F. What Makes You Beautiful.

PAGE 31 - Spot the Difference:

PAGE 14 - True or False:
1.TRUE 2. FALSE 3. FALSE 4. TRUE
5. FALSE 6. TRUE 7. TRUE 8. FALSE
9. FALSE 10. FALSE

PAGE 15 - Tell the One Direction Story:
Harry, Liam, Niall, Zayn and Louis
auditioned for The X Factor separately, but
the Judges asked them to form a group.
They were surprised, but they all knew that
they had to take the opportunity. Before long
they were best friends.

The boys had a fantastic time on the show,
and although they came third, they were
already getting bags of fan mail! It was clear
that One Direction had an exciting future
ahead. When they were signed to Simon
Cowell's record company, they knew that
their dreams had come true.

One Direction went on tour across the UK
and Ireland, and everywhere they went they
gained more fans. They released their first
album Up All Night in autumn 2011, and
their first single 'What Makes You Beautiful'
became the biggest pre-order in Sony's single
history. It went in at number one in the UK
and Irish charts as soon as it was on iTunes.

Next, the guys set out to conquer America.
Fans lined the streets wherever they went,
and in March 2012, Up All Night entered the
US Billboard 200 chart at number one. The
boys had cracked the States.

All across the world, people went One Direction
mad! Up All Night went to number one in
15 countries. With more tours planned and
another album in the pipeline, One Direction
has truly become a global phenomenon!

PAGE 20 - Starstruck
• Zayn didn't go to meet Johnny Depp
• Liam Tweeted a snap of himself with Jay Z
• Niall gets starstruck by American
  First Lady, Michelle Obama

PAGES 39 - Odd One Out:
Number 4

PAGE 40 - Star Sudoku:

PAGE 41 - Missing Lyrics:
Missing words, line by line are...
1. Hand, 2. Made, 3. Bear, 4. Be, 5. Dots,
6. Freckles, 7. Sense, 8. Loved, 9. crinkles,
smile, 10. Thighs, 11. Dimples, your,
12. Endlessly, 13. Slip, mouth, 14. You,
15. Oh, add, 16. Cup of tea, 17. Talk ,
18. Conversations, secrets, 19. No, 20. Voice,
21. Want, 22. Weigh, 23. Squeeze, 24. Half,
25. Treat, darling, 26. Here, 27. like.

ANSWERS

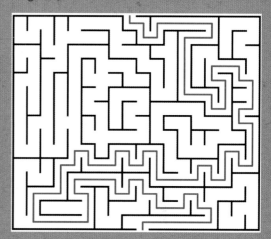

A	B	C	D	E	F	T	H	I	J	K	L	M	N	O
D	J	S	G	K	L	O	U	I	S	F	X	N	P	R
J	W	U	T	S	E	U	M	C	A	M	T	S	D	I
I	D	A	D	S	A	R	R	O	R	R	U	P	O	T
L	I	A	M	G	B	I	E	M	S	F	G	B	F	E
S	R	N	W	S	E	M	I	P	O	N	T	T	L	R
F	E	Y	H	I	E	S	M	E	O	H	Q	W	S	A
J	C	E	B	M	G	A	S	T	G	O	F	I	V	U
G	T	K	Z	A	Y	N	H	I	N	F	J	T	K	O
H	I	S	R	B	A	M	N	T	U	H	F	T	L	D
G	O	M	L	F	F	L	N	I	G	F	D	E	Y	V
S	N	G	R	B	L	K	J	O	N	H	A	R	R	Y
D	E	X	Q	A	N	S	I	N	G	I	N	G	I	D
W	R	G	P	J	M	I	Y	T	F	E	F	G	C	J
E	S	U	B	J	Y	T	N	I	A	L	L	J	S	G

A. Zayn, B. Liam, C. Harry,
D. Louis, E. Niall

PAGES 50 - Prank You Very Much:
Louis likes to play the following pranks on sleeping band mates...
1. Sticking drinking straws up their noses.
2. Waking them up by throwing a bucket of water over them.
3. Putting one of their hands into a bowl of water to make them pee themselves.

PAGES 54 - Love, Love, Love:
1. ELEANOR CALDER - Louis
2. PERRIE EDWARDS - Zayn
3. AMY GREEN - Niall
4. REBECCA FERGUSON - Zayn
5. LEONA LEWIS - Liam
6. TAYLOR SWIFT - Harry
7. CAROLINE FLACK - Harry
8. DANIELLE PEAZER - Liam
9. DEMI LOVATO - Niall
10. CARA DELEVINGNE – Niall

1. Harry, 2. Niall and Liam, 3. Zayn,
4. Louis

Page 81 - Quizzical Quotes:
1. Zayn, 2. Niall, 3. Louis,
4. Liam, 5. Harry

Pages 82 - Picture Perfect:
A. Harry, B. Zayn,
C. Louis, D. Liam, E. Louis,
F. Niall, G. Zayn, H. Liam

PAGES 84 - Whose Tattoos?
Harry – A pair of swallows, Birdcage, Theatre masks, 'Won't stop til we surrender', 'Things I can', 'Things I can't', 17 Black, a capital A, Padlock, Large star. Two screws.

Zayn – Microphone, 'Zap', crossed fingers, 'Be true to who you are', 'Walter', A silver fern, a playing card, two screws.
Louis – Two screws, a stick man skateboarding.

Liam – Two screws, 'Everything I ever wanted, but nothing I'll ever need', Four chevrons

• Niall was, to date still tattoo-less, but had joked about having tattoos on his buttocks.
• Ed Sheeran tattooed Harry with a padlock design.

Page 86 - Anagrams:
1. Carl Falk, 2. Steve Mac,
3. Rami Yacoub, 4. Matt Squire,
5. Shellback, 6. Julian Bunett

Page 87 - Name the Song:
Another World, Gotta Be You, I Would, Little Things, Live While We're Young, Moments, More Than This, Na Na Na, One Thing, What Makes You Beautiful.

Pages 90 - In-Depth Directioner
1. Harry Edward Styles,
2. Louis 3. 15 4. 24th December 1991
5. Bootcamp, 6. Niall, 7. Harry,
8. 'What Makes You Beautiful', 9. Virgo,
10. Liam, 11. @Harry_Styles, 12. 2010
13. Mullingar, Ireland. 14. The Watford Colosseum, 15. Zayn Javadd Malik

Page 94 - Coded Message:
Hey Directioners, we'd like to thank you for all your amazing support over the past year. You mean everything to us. Stay cool!

Page 102 - Memory Test:
1. Harry, 2. Liam, 3. His left,
4. Niall and Liam, 5. Louis 6. Three
7. Beige, 8. To his right, 9. Cream, grey and yellow, 10. Trees

ONE DIRECTION